Introduction

The first part of the *National Trust Walker's Notebook* offers some enticements to get you out and about exploring the rich and varied landscapes of England, Wales and Northern Ireland. We have gathered together some recommended walks of varying type and length, and to suit different abilities. A detailed walking leaflet for each route is available to download from our website (www.nationaltrust.org.uk/walks). All of these walks are in landscapes which are in the ownership and care of the National Trust. We look forward to greeting you as you venture on your walk at these or the many other sites under our protection.

The National Trust was established in 1895 to 'promote the permanent preservation of places of natural beauty or historic interest'. Since then it has secured these landscapes through purchase, often with the help of appeals, or by gift. They are held in trust for the benefit of the nation.

So whether you are interested in wildlife or woodland, the coast or countryside, there will be something for everyone, whatever the weather.

The second part of the *National Trust Walker's Notebook* is where you can record and remember your own walks, whether they are on National Trust land or elsewhere.

A good pair of boots, layers of clothing, a map and you're off....

Coastal heath (Common heather, Bell heather and Western gorse) in late summer on the cliff tops of Highveer Point, above Heddon's Mouth near Lynton, looking along the north Devon coast, at sunset. (Devon)

Walking: Come Prepared

What should I bring?

- Comfortable footwear with sturdy soles. Walking boots/shoes are the best option, but wear them around the house before venturing outdoors in them for the first time.
- In hot sunny weather pack a hat, sun glasses, suncream and an extra large bottle of water.
- In cold weather, dress up warm. Wear lots of layers, gloves and a scarf.
- Try to avoid wearing bright colours or anything that rustles as you walk along (you might scare away wildlife).
- A camera or notebook and pencil to jot down what you see, a map and compass, binoculars and a field guide to identify the wildlife you encounter!
- Walking poles can be useful, particularly for more strenuous routes.

National Trust
Walker's Notebook

F

FRANCES LINCOLN LIMITED
PUBLISHERS

Frances Lincoln Limited
4 Torriano Mews
Torriano Avenue
London NW5 2RZ
www.franceslincoln.com

National Trust Walker's Notebook
Copyright © Frances Lincoln Limited
2009

Text and illustrations copyright © 2009
National Trust (Enterprises) Limited

Produced under Licence from The
National Trust (Enterprises) Ltd.

A catalogue record for this book is
available from the British Library

ISBN: 978-0-7112-2999-0

First Frances Lincoln edition 2009

9 8 7 6 5 4 3 2 1

For more information please visit:
www.nationaltrust.org.uk

Watersmeet

The Countryside Code

Respect, Protect, Enjoy

- Check weather forecasts before you leave and do not be afraid to turn back.
- Follow local signs, advice and observe any access restrictions.
- Leave gates and property as you find them.
- Litter can be dangerous to wildlife and farm animals – take rubbish away with you.
- Remember that rocks, plants and trees are homes and food for insects, birds and animals so do not damage them.
- Wild animals and farm animals can behave unpredictably, especially if they are with their young, so always give them plenty of space.
- Consider others – drive carefully on country lanes and give way to walkers when you are on a bike.

Ladybirds on grasses at Brancaster Harbour early in the morning. (Norfolk)

Dogs in the Countryside

Dogs and dog walkers are welcome at National Trust coast and countryside sites, but we do suffer problems in some places when a minority of thoughtless dog owners cause trouble for other visitors and vulnerable wildlife.

Please:

- Clear up after your dog by bagging and taking dog refuse away with you or using the bins provided.
- Keep your dog under close control at all times.
- Observe local notices on the need to keep dogs on a lead at sensitive times of the year e.g. during the breeding season for ground-nesting birds or when sheep are lambing or deer are having calves.
- Abide by seasonal access restrictions on popular beaches in the summer.
- Dogs can easily overheat so never leave them in cars on hot days.

Where access for dogs has been restricted, particularly on some popular beaches in the summer, the National Trust attempts to find suitable alternative locations for dog walking nearby.

Tick Bites and Lyme Disease

Come spring and summer we all want to get outside, enjoy the weather and explore beautiful places. If you are visiting woodland or heathland areas, it is important to be aware of the risk of tick bites.

Reports show there has been a rise in the number of people infected by ticks carrying Lyme disease (*Lyme borreliosis*), particularly in Exmoor, the New Forest, the South Downs, parts of Wiltshire and Berkshire, the Lake District and the Yorkshire moors. Peak times for tick bites are late spring, early summer and autumn.

Be tick aware:

- Always wear long-sleeved shirts (fastened at the cuffs) and trousers (with socks tucked into shoes) when walking through tall vegetation.
- Light coloured fabrics are useful, as it is easier to see ticks against a light background. Consider using insect repellent on your clothes.
- Inspect skin frequently and make sure that children's head and neck areas, including scalps, are properly checked. At the end of the day, check again for ticks, especially in skin folds.
- Check that ticks are not brought home on clothes and that pets do not bring unfed ticks into the home on their fur.
- If you do get bitten, remove any attached ticks carefully.
- If you are concerned in any way or become unwell, see your doctor as soon as possible.

Top Tips for Observing Wildlife

Before you go
- Do some research about the habitats and wildlife in the area you are going to visit.
- Decide ahead of time where and when you will go. Many flowers, fungi and animals can only be seen at certain times of year.

Take with you
- An illustrated pocket field guide to help you identify plants or animals on the spot.
- A pair of binoculars. This will allow you to keep your distance from wildlife and therefore they are less likely to take fright and leave.
- A camera.
- A small tripod (or lean on a steady rock), you will get a much less blurry, shaky image of your wildlife than if you are holding your binoculars or camera.
- A magnifying glass for checking out insects and flowers, leaves, fungi or lichen.
- This notebook and pencil so you can describe what you see and hear – draw a simple field sketch, rub in a bit of soil or press a leaf between the pages to remind you of the place.

Reduce your visibility
Many animals have very good eyesight and if they see you approach they will hide or run away, so be as quiet as possible.
- Avoid bright colours and wear natural or neutral-coloured clothing and rucksacks.
- Be careful that sunlight does not reflect off glasses and equipment.

- Check whether you are blocking out the sun when approaching insects as they will get disturbed when your shadow falls across them.

Keep the sound down
Many animals have an amazing sense of hearing and if they hear you approach they will hide or run away, so be as quiet as possible.
- Watch where you place your feet so as not to snap twigs or create other sudden noises.
- Make sure that your rucksack and pockets do not rustle.
- If you are going to sit still for some time to watch wildlife, then open all of your food packets as soon as you arrive in order to avoid making noise later on.

Minimize your smells
Many animals have an amazing sense of smell and will keep away if they can whiff something unusual.
- Avoid using strong-scented perfumes, shampoos, or suntan lotions.
- The smell of washing powder can also alert wildlife to you, so wear or air your clothes for several days outside to absorb natural scents.
- Check the wind direction is not blowing your smell towards the wildlife you're spotting – change your position to adjust for this.
- Never smoke!

Get comfortable
Watching wildlife can take time, you need to be patient and wait quietly. The more comfortable you are, the less likely you will be to move around and scare things.

- Take a rug, foam or inflatable roll mat to sit or lie on.
- Even in summer it can get chilly in windy outdoor places and just staying still for a while can reduce your body heat – bring cosy layers of clothing in any season.

Listen really carefully

- Close your eyes for a minute or two and let your hearing take control of your senses.
- Cup your hands to your ears to hear better and to determine the direction of the sound.
- You will hear many more birds than you can ever see. Different species have different birdsongs, so they are a really useful clue to help identify which is which.

Think like your subject

Understanding a bit about the living patterns of wildlife can enable you to choose where to go and at what time of the day. Field guides should give details about animals' behaviour, but here are some general hints.

- Go to areas that are regularly visited by wildlife – places to get a drink, places to shelter from the wind, good viewpoints, sunny glades in woodlands.
- Flowering plants or shrubs attract insects and fruiting trees or bushes attract birds or insects.
- Is it the time of year when animals will be looking for a mate, nesting in a tree or underground, feeding for winter or preparing to migrate?
- Like humans many animals are less active during the hottest part of the day, but insects and butterflies are mostly likely to be out pollinating flowers when the weather is warm and sunny.

- Dawn and dusk are good times to see and hear foxes, birds and bats – get up early or go to bed late to spot them!
- After heavy rain, many animals emerge to feed on the flooded out insects and worms.

Conserve what you enjoy for others to enjoy too

- Leave wildlife where it belongs – in the wild! Never take creatures home with you.
- Leave the area as clean as or cleaner than you found it. Always carry a rubbish bag so you can take your rubbish home with you.
- Avoid going near nests or burrows during breeding seasons – especially with a dog. If you disturb wildlife here returning parents may be scared away, causing them to abandon their eggs or young. Keep your distance, follow signs and use binoculars.

The view from Mam Tor looking north west takes in the popular ridge walk to Hollins Cross, Back Tor and Lose Hill. To the north is Esdale and south the Castleton Valley obscured by mist. (Derbyshire & Peak District)

Directory of Walks

For each of these routes the National Trust has created a simple walking leaflet with a map, route directions and highlights to look out for on the way. These can be downloaded from the website (www.nationaltrust.org.uk/walks), printed and taken along with you the next time you visit. The directory is organised according to the National Trust regions.

DEVON & CORNWALL

Cornwall

Cubert, West Pentire and Crantock Bay
Wildlife walk, 6 miles (9.6 km)

The coastline just south of Newquay is incredibly varied with fantastic displays of arable flora in summer. At West Pentire see whole fields scarlet with poppies and other rare meadow plants. There is also lots of sandy grassland, rich in wildflowers like cowslip and pyramidal orchid. The dunes behind Holywell Bay are the home for hundreds of different insects and great for bug hunting. This is truly a walk for all seasons: visit in autumn for a privileged view of grey seal pups and winter to find migrant birds in the fields.

Start point: West Pentire car park – OS Landranger 200: SW775605

The Lizard

Coastal walk, 4½ miles (7.2 km)

This walk around the Lizard Peninsula, the southerly tip of mainland Britain, takes in dramatic cliff scenery, rare wild flowers and an interesting coastal history. Kynance Cove has a sandy beach and islands of serpentine stone.

Maps and start grid ref: Kynance Cove – OS Landranger 203 map – grid ref SW 703125.

Dodman Point

Coastal walk, 3 miles (4.8 km)

Dodman Point is the highest headland on the south Cornish coast. You will walk through a landscape formed by 4,000 years of human occupation.

Maps and start grid ref: OS Landranger 204 gr SW999404, Explorer 105

Gribbin Head, Fowey

Coastal walk, 5 miles (8 km)

A walk along coast famed for its association with Daphne du Maurier, and the setting of many of her books. This area of south-east Cornish coast offers breathtaking natural beauty and includes a variety of beaches, coves, woodlands and grassland rich in wild flowers.

Maps and start grid ref: OS Landranger 200 gr SX173518, Explorer 107

A view of The Gribbin. (Cornwall)

Lansallos
Coastal walk, 4 miles (6.4 km)
A walk along a magnificent stretch of south-east Cornwall coast, dotted with secluded coves and beaches. Inland, the walk passes through traditional farmland.
Maps and start grid ref: OS Landranger 201 gr SX173517, Explorer 107

Tintagel
Coastal walk, 5 miles (8 km)
Tintagel on the north Cornish coast is steeped in Arthurian legend. This walk takes in some spectacular coastline. Start at The Old Post Office and as you make your way along the path, make sure to look for Barras Nose.
Maps and start grid ref: OS Landranger 200, grid ref: SX 051888

Devon

Froward Point
Coastal walk, 3 miles (4.8 km)
Froward Point near the mouth of the River Dart offers both nature and history for the walker. This walk includes spectacular coastal views.
Maps and start grid ref: OS Landranger 202 gr SX904510, Explorer 20E

Heddon Valley
Coastal walk, 2 miles (3.2 km)
A comfortable walk down to the sea and back from the Hunter's Inn following the Heddon River through sessile oak woods and river meadows.
Maps and start grid ref: OS Landranger 180 gr SS655483, Explorer OL 9

Heddon Valley and Woody Bay
Coastal walk, 6 miles (9.6 km)
This walk takes in views to the south Wales, Devon and Somerset coasts.
Maps and start grid ref: OS Landranger 180 gr SS655483, Explorer OL 9

Little Dartmouth
Coastal walk, 3 miles (4.8 km)
With views over the River Dart estuary, this walk takes in cliffs where peregrine hunt, as well as a civil war fort.
Maps and start grid ref: OS Landranger 202 gr SX874491, Explorer OL20

The coastline at Froward Point. (Devon)

Ayrmer Cove, Ringmore

Coastal views and countryside walk, 3 miles (4.8 km)

Explore the beauty and remoteness of the Ringmore Valley on this journey through old smugglers' lanes and down to an unspoilt, secluded cove, boasting magnificent coastal views. Return through fields and woodlands rich in wildlife.

Maps and start grid ref: Ayrmer Cove car park – grid ref: SX649456 – map: OS Explorer OL20

Sharptor to Bolt Head

Coastal walk, 3½ miles (5.6 km)

A beautiful walk in spectacular scenery at the mouth of the Salcombe estuary on the south Dorset coast, with plenty of wildlife and archaeology to enjoy.

Maps and start grid ref: OS Landranger 202 gr SX729375, Explorer 20 E&W

Snapes Point

Coastal walk, 1½ miles (2.4 km)

An easy walk in a gentle landscape beside the beautiful Kingsbridge Estuary on the south Devon coast which offers good bird watching opportunities.

Maps and start grid ref: OS Landranger 202 gr SX739401, Explorer 20 E&W

Woodhuish Farm, Scabbacombe

Coastal walk, 3 miles (4.8 km)

This dramatic walk offers a range of landscape features and habitats. Wetlands, cliffs and rolling farmland are all to be enjoyed.

Maps and start grid ref: OS Landranger 202 gr SX913530, Explorer OL20

Baggy Point & Woolacombe Bay

Coastal walk, 6½ miles (10.4 km)

This spectacular walk along the Woolacombe beach includes cliff-top views and secluded beaches. Wander along the wide-open spaces of the sandy beach towards Putsborough Sand. Make a detour to Baggy Point and take in the views out to sea.

Maps and start grid ref: OS Landranger 180 gr SS 447 407

Watersmeet

Hill forts and rivers, 6 miles (9.6 km)

Dramatic scenery, fast-flowing rivers and ancient woodland, all feature on this tranquil walk through west Exmoor. The area is home to a rich variety of wildlife from butterflies to red deer.

Maps and start grid ref: Countisbury car park – grid ref: SS 747497 – maps: OS Landranger 168 & Explorer 196

EAST OF ENGLAND

Cambridgeshire

Wicken Fen

Wildlife walk, 3 miles (4.8 km)

Explore a unique fragment of the wilderness that once covered East Anglia on this easy walk. Wicken Fen is the National Trust's oldest nature reserve, a great place to look out for wild konik ponies, plus a variety of rare plants, insects and birds.

Maps and start grid ref: Wicken Fen National Trust Visitor Centre – OS Landranger 154 – grid ref: TL563705

Norfolk

Blakeney to Stiffkey

Coastal wildlife walk, 4 miles (6.4 km)

Enjoy Norfolk's vast open landscape and big skies on this lovely walk along the coast path beside pristine saltmarsh. Remember to bring your binoculars, as there are lots of wildlife-spotting opportunities across the marshes and scrub. Four miles (6.4 km) is one way.

Maps and start grid ref: Bus stop near Blakeney Church (grid ref: TG032436) or Blakeney Quay (TG028442) Maps: Landranger 132 /133 and Explorer 251

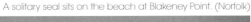
A solitary seal sits on the beach at Blakeney Point. (Norfolk)

Suffolk

Flatford Bridge Cottage and Dedham Vale

In an artist's footsteps, 4 miles (6.4 km) plus optional 3-mile (4.8 km) loop to Dedham

Follow in the footsteps of John Constable and get a feel for the trees, rivers, sounds and light that inspired one of the greatest British painters of all time.

Maps and start grid ref: OS Landranger 168, Explorer 196, TM 093 322

Orford Ness

Nature reserve, 5½ miles (8.8 km)

A walk around this important nature reserve and former secret military test site.

Maps and start grid ref: Orford Quay – grid ref: TM 429494 – maps: OS Landranger 169, Explorer 212

EAST MIDLANDS

Derbyshire

Hayfields to Kinder Scout

Historic route walk, 8 miles (12.8 km)

Follow in the footsteps of the 500 walkers who took part in the 1932 mass trespass to secure access to the countryside for all. This walk enables you to retrace their historic route, and tells their story and explains more about how the National Trust cares for the Peak District today.

Maps and start grid ref: OS Landranger 110, Explorer OL1, grid ref: SK 048869 (Bowden Bridge)

Kinder Scout

Countryside walk, 7½ miles (12 km)

This challenging and exhilarating walk takes you high up on the windswept Kinder plateau, one of the great upland areas of the gritstone 'Dark Peak'. Enjoy spectacular views across the Vale of Edale, explore mysterious rock formations and look out for a fantastic range of moorland wildlife.

Maps and start grid ref: Edale – OS Explorer Map OL1 – grid ref SK 124856

Calke Park and Abbey

Wildlife walk, 1½ miles (2.4 km)

A peaceful walk in this National Nature Reserve and historic country park estate. Keep your eyes open for the Old Man of

Ilam Country Park in the South Peak District (Derbyshire & Peak District)

Calke, signs of badgers in the woods and colourful dragonflies darting around the ponds.

Maps and start grid ref: OS Landranger 128: SK367226; Postcode: DE73 7LE

Ilam Park to Dovedale Stepping Stones

Peak District walk, 2½ mile (4 km) round trip

Discover the limestone countryside of the southern Peak District, famed for its wildlife and geology. Starting at the tranquil Victorian landscape and woodland of Ilam Park, this easy walk takes you into Dovedale, an iconic and spectacular gorge carved out by the river Dove.

Maps and start grid ref: Ilam Park – grid ref: SK 131507 – map:
OS Landranger 119 & Explorer 259

Northamptonshire

Canons Ashby

History and wildlife walk, ⅝ mile (1 km)

Most people come to the Elizabethan Manor house at Canons Ashby and overlook the parkland right on its doorstep.

Maps and start grid ref: Canons Ashby car park – grid ref: SP577506 –
OS Landranger map 152

Nottinghamshire

Clumber Park

Chapel, Temple and Ashes trail, 1½ miles (2.4 km)

Clumber was the country estate of the Dukes of Newcastle and, although the mansion was demolished in 1938, the chapel, pleasure ground, lake and walled garden remain as clues to its grand past. Explore the parkland on this easy trail to uncover Clumber's past and enjoy a little wildlife-spotting along the way.

Maps and start grid ref: National Trust Clumber Park car park – OS Landranger 120 – grid ref: SK625745

NORTH WEST

Cheshire

Alderley Edge

Woodland walk, 4½ miles (7.2 km)

This beautiful woodland walk begins at Alderley Edge railway station and is just 12 miles (19.3 km) south of Manchester. Set around a dramatic sandstone escarpment in rolling Cheshire farmland and mature Scots pines and beech woodlands, the Edge has spectacular views, intriguing legends and an ancient history of copper mining which dates back 4,000 years to the Bronze Age.

Maps and start grid ref: Alderley Edge railway station Map: OS 118/268 Grid ref: SJ843785

Cumbria

Buttermere to Rannerdale

Fell, Lake and Woodland walk, 3 miles (4.8 km)

This exhilarating Lakeland ridge walk climbs from the Buttermere Valley up to the summit of Rannerdale Knotts. Though it's one of the smaller and more rounded Cumbrian fells, it gives stunning views over three lakes and many high peaks. Our route returns via the shoreline of Crummock Water and Nether How woodland to the pretty little village of Buttermere.

Maps and start grid ref: NT car park at Buttermere, Landranger 90 & Explorer OI4 NY172172

Tarn Hows and Monk Coniston

Wildlife walk, 3½ miles or 5 miles (5.6 km or 8 km)

Pass through iconic Lake District farm and woodland on this two-option route created by a 19th-century industrialist to wow guests at his country estate. The circuit of Tarn Hows is an 'all-ability' trail.

Maps and start grid ref: Monk Coniston car park – OS Explorer 7 – grid reference: 316978v

Seathwaite to Sty Head and Grains Gill

5½ miles (8.8 km)

An invigorating walk along an ancient pack horse route in the heart of the Lake District, offering a spectacular landscape of rugged crags and refreshing tarns.

Maps and start grid ref: Seathwaite – grid ref: NY 235121 – OS Landranger 90 or Explorer OI4

View across Crummock Water by Buttermere Valley. (Cumbria)

Townend and Troutbeck Valley

A Beatrix Potter favourite, 4 miles (6.4 km)

Discover one of Beatrix Potter's favourite places in the Lake District on this walk through the Troutbeck Valley. There is lots to see along the way including the charming 17th-century farmhouse, Townend.

Maps and start grid ref: Brockhole Visitor Centre – grid ref. NY407023 – OS Landranger 90, Explorer OL7

Lancashire

Arnside Knott

Wildlife coastal walk, 2 miles (3.2 km)

A walk up to a hill ridge with fantastic views overlooking Morecombe Bay on one side and the Lake District on the other. Listen for the loud 'pichoo' call of the marsh tit in the woodland and look out for rare butterflies.

Maps and start grid ref: OS Landranger 97:SD450774; OS Explorer OL7

Silverdale

Coastal walk, 2 miles (3.2 km)

Coastal cliffs are a rarity around Morecambe Bay so Heald Brow and Jack Scout are especially interesting and attractive. Scrub provides good sites for breeding song birds such as whitethroat, linnet and garden warbler. The limestone grassland is notable for many flowers which support many species of butterflies in the summer months such as brimstone, large skippers, small heaths and some of the rarer 'fritillary' butterflies.

Maps and start grid ref: OS Landranger 97 gr SD465754, Explorer OL7

Merseyside

Formby

Red squirrel walk, 1.8 miles (2.9 km)

This walk through the pinewoods of Formby is a great starting point for walks along the Sefton Coastal Path. There are stunning views of Sefton's natural coast with its golden sand dunes and wide sandy beaches. You may even catch a glimpse of a rare red squirrel in the pinewoods.

Maps and start grid ref: SD 281 082, OS Explorer 285

SOUTH EAST

East Sussex

Nap Wood

Woodland walk, 1 mile (1.6 km)

Discover a tranquil woodland oasis along an ancient track way of the Weald. Nap Wood is home to a fantastic array of wildlife, from the mature trees that tower above you to the vivid displays of bluebells that decorate the woodland floor in late spring. See what you can spot on this gentle one mile walk.

Maps and start grid ref: A267 layby – grid ref: TQ 581329 – OS Explorer 136 or Landranger 188 maps

Birling Gap to Crowlink

Coastal walk, 4½ miles (7.2 km)

A lovely walk in the high summer on part of the Seven Sisters with plenty of wild flowers to see, full of historical interest and beautiful views along the Sussex coast. The last part of the walk is the smugglers' route from East Dean to Birling Gap.

Maps and start grid ref: OS Landranger 199 g.r. TV555959, Explorer 123

Kent

The White Cliffs of Dover

Wildlife coastal walk, 4 miles (6.4 km)

The White Cliffs of Dover in Kent are one of the most iconic stretches of coast in the UK. This route will give the walker a sense of military history through the centuries.

Maps and start grid ref: TR336422 – OS Landranger 179 and Explorer 138

St Margaret's, Dover (circular walk)

Coastal walk, 2½ miles (4 km)

A short walk in St Margaret's at Cliffe, full of historical and some literary connections, including a short section along the White Cliffs of Dover. On clear days there are views across to France.

Maps and start grid ref: OS Landranger 179 gr TR368445, Explorer 138

St Margaret's, Dover (Kingsdown walk)

Coastal walk, 4 miles (6.4 km)

There are fantastic views across the Channel to France on this walk. The route, along this very important strategic coastline in the defence of Great Britain, passes plenty of historical interest.

Maps and start grid ref: OS Landranger 179 gr TR368445, Explorer 138

Sprivers Wood

Woodland walk, 1 mile (1.6 km)

Travel back to the 18th century as you enjoy this gentle walk through Sprivers Wood in the heart of the High Weald. Unearth signs of the estate's World War Two activity and spot a whole host of wildlife, from butterflies to dormice.

Maps and start grid ref: A267 lay-by – grid ref: TQ 694404 – maps: Explorer 136 & Landranger 188

West Sussex

Ditchling Beacon to Devil's Dyke

Countryside walk, 5 miles (8 km)

This walk takes in one of the most stunning sections of the South Downs Way long distance trail. Spring and summer bring an abundance of wildflowers into bloom. The richness of the plant life is thanks to the chalk soil which forms a unique grassland habitat.

Maps and start grid ref: Ditchling Beacon – grid ref: TQ 332113 – map: OS Landranger 198

Harting Down

Wildlife walk, 2 miles (3.2 km)

One of the largest areas of ancient chalk downland in National Trust care, Harting Down in West Sussex is a renowned nature reserve and Site of Special Scientific Interest. Sheep grazing helps conserve this grassland environment where rare wildlife thrives. This walk offers panoramic views over the Weald to the North Downs, before descending into secluded valleys of natural and historic interest.

Maps and start grid ref: OS Landranger 197: SU791180

East Head

Coastal walk, 2 miles (3.2 km)

East Head is a natural, constantly evolving sand and shingle spit. This walk encapsulates the challenges faced by the Trust in managing a dynamic, ever-changing site.

Maps and start grid ref: OS Landranger 197 gr SZ768981, Explorer 120

THAMES & SOLENT

Buckinghamshire

Ashridge Estate

Wildlife walk, 2 miles (3.2 km)

On the main ridge of the magnificent Chiltern Hills, there are over 2,000 hectares of open countryside, chalk downland and woodland to explore and escape to at Ashridge. This range of habitats means there's plenty of wildlife (the estate is renowned for butterflies and wildflowers). Bluebell displays in spring are superb and you can find lots of grassland flowers like orchids. Autumn is a great time to watch deer rut and enjoy the golden hues.

Maps and start grid ref: OS Explorer 181: SP970130 (Ashridge Visitor Centre)

Postcode: HP4 1LX

Ashridge Estate. (Hertfordshire)

Hughenden (red walk)
Countryside walk, 4 miles (6.4 km)
Discover the wonderful and varied landscape of Hughenden Valley as you wander about this historic estate that was once home to Victorian prime minister, Benjamin Disraeli. This walk explores colourful beech woods and pastures, visiting the Disraeli monument and the church where 'Dizzy' is buried along the way.
Maps and start grid ref: Hughenden Manor ticket office – grid ref: SU866955 – map: OS Landranger 165

Hughenden (purple walk)
German forest walk, 2½ miles (4 km)
Explore the dark evergreen woods of Hughenden estate, inspired by Disraeli's visits to Germany's Black Forest.
Maps and start grid ref: Landranger 165, Explorer 172: SU866955

Hampshire

The Vyne
Woodland walk, 2¼ miles (3.7 km)
This gentle walk explores Morgaston Woods, part of The Vyne estate in Hampshire. Along the way you'll discover ancient trees, wildlife-rich wetlands and medieval fishponds.
Maps and start grid ref: Middle Gate, Morgaston Road – map: OS Landranger 175/186 – grid ref: SU625572

Oxfordshire

Watlington Hill
Wildlife walk, 1½ miles (2.4 km)
Discover an Oxfordshire dreamscape as you walk to the top of Watlington Hill, with fine views and fine wildlife, all year round. A mosaic of short rabbit turf, scrub and dense yew woodland, make it an especially good site for butterflies, with a large population of silver-spotted skipper flying here from late July to early September. This is also a super spot for picnics – just watch butterflies flutter and red kites soar overhead as you tuck in.
Maps and start grid ref: Watlington Hill – NT car park – OS Landranger map 175 – grid ref: SU710935

White Horse Hill to Ashdown
Countryside walk, 7½ miles (12 km)
Enjoy a walk across the ancient chalk downs of Oxfordshire and

absorb the history found along this enigmatic stretch of the ancient Ridgeway. Encompassing Neolithic history to World War Two inhabitants.

Maps and start grid ref: OS Landranger 174, Explorer 170 SU293866

Isle of Wight

Borthwood Copse

Red squirrel walk, 1 mile (1.6 km)

Red squirrels live in several locations on the Isle of Wight and the ancient woodland of Borthwood Copse, near Sandown, is one of them. On this short walk you might see a glimpse of red, or just enjoy the fine oak and beech trees, which stand amongst glades of sweet chestnut and hazel.

Maps and start grid ref: OS Landranger 196 gr SZ 570 844, Explorer OL29

WESSEX

Dorset

Brownsea Island

Wildlife walk, 1 mile (1.6 km)

There are approximately 200–250 red squirrels on Brownsea Island and you stand a good chance of seeing one on this walk through the woodland that they live in.

Maps and start grid ref: OS Explorer OL15: SZ022876; OS Landranger 195

Dancing Ledge

Coastal walk, 4 miles (6.4 km)

This walk highlights current and past farming practices, the legacy of quarry areas, interesting buildings and wildlife, all seen along an impressive stretch of the Jurassic Coast.

Maps and start grid ref: OS Landranger 195 gr SY997784, Explorer OL15

Old Harry Rocks

Coastal walk, 3½ miles (5.6 km)

Old Harry Rocks is one of the most famous landmarks on the south coast. This great circular walk starts at the beach at Studland and follows the Jurassic Coastline to the tip of the impressive chalk cliffs of Old Harry Rocks.

Maps and start grid ref: OS Landranger 195 gr SZ 036 824

Old Harry Rocks at Studland, part of the Corfe Castle Estate. (Dorset)

West Bexington

Coastal walk, 2½ miles (4 km)

A beautiful walk along part of the Jurassic Coast, between Bridport and Weymouth. The walk passes through farmland rich in wildlife to the ever changing backdrop of the sea. There is plenty to see with farmland birds and flowers, and recent history along the route with the backdrop of the ever changing seascape from Devon to Portland Bill. Not all the walk is on National Trust land.

Maps and start grid ref: OS Landranger 194 gr SY532865, Explorer OL15

Stonebarrow Hill to Golden Cap

Coastal walk, 4½ miles (7.2 km)

Explore England's first natural World Heritage Site, the Jurassic Coastline, on this stunning mile walk through wildlife-rich countryside. The autumn sunlight on the Golden Cap's rocky cliffs changes their colour to a beautiful rusty-gold hue, hence its name.

Maps and start grid ref: OS Sheet 193, SY383933

Corfe Common & Corfe Castle

Historical footsteps walk, 1½ miles (2.4 km)

This gentle short walk explores Corfe Common, a sandstone ridge south of the picturesque village of Corfe Castle. Look out for signs of the human activity that shaped this interesting archaeological landscape over thousands of years and enjoy the wide range of wildlife which now makes its home here.

Maps and start grid ref: Corfe Castle ticket office – OS Explorer OL15 map – grid ref. SW961821

Gloucestershire

Sherborne Park

Sculpture trail, 4 miles (6.4 km)

Sherborne Park Estate, set in lovely rolling countryside and the village of Sherborne next to the river Windrush, offers something for all. This circular sign-posted walk takes you through a woodland sculpture trail, farmland, woods and down to the village of Sherborne. It is a fun walk for people of all ages.

Maps and start grid ref: OS 163, SP158143 (parking for estate walks)

Woodchester Park

Countryside walk, 3½ miles (5.6 km)

Set in a Gloucestershire valley near Stroud, Woodchester Park includes the remains of an 18th- and 19th-century designed landscape, a chain of five lakes and fine woodland. This walk along the orange trail to the Boathouse gives a great introduction to this tranquil, historic place.

Maps and start grid ref: OS 162, SO797012

Somerset

Bin Combe, Exmoor

Extreme butterflying, 1½ miles (2.4 km)

This one is tough, very tough. The habitat is tall, dense bracken on steep slopes where there are no paths, but this is by far the best place to go in pursuit of the rare heath fritillary butterfly. Welcome to the world of extreme butterflying near Dunkery Beacon in the north of the Exmoor National Park!

Maps and start grid ref: Dunkery Beacon car park – OS Landranger 181, Explorer 9 – grid ref: SS905410

Brean Down

Coastal Walk, 3 miles (4.8 km)

Discover one of the great landmarks of the Somerset coastline on this scenic coastal walk across Brean Down. Standing over 300 feet high and extending one and a half miles into the Bristol Channel, the Down is steeped in intriguing stories, from prehistoric worship to World War Two weapon testing. It's also renowned for its wildlife; so keep a look out for a great variety of birds, plants and butterflies en route!

Maps and start grid ref: Cove Café – grid ref: ST 296588 – maps: OS Landranger 182, Explorer 153

Bossington

Coastal walk, 5½ miles (8.8 km)

Bossington in north Somerset provides the ideal point for views across the Bristol Channel. This walk takes in the ever-changing coastline in this picturesque part of the West Country.

Maps and start grid ref: OS Landranger 181 gr SS 898 489

Collard Hill

Butterfly walk 1½ miles (2.4 km)

In 2002 Collard Hill was opened by the National Trust on behalf of the Large Blue Partnership as a great place for the public to come and see this rare and fascinating butterfly. Having disappeared from the UK in the late 1970s, the large blue is flourishing here and even at busy weekends, you'll find plenty of quiet spots in which you can get a good glimpse of them! Collard Hill is a great picnic spot with fantastic views from the ridge.

Maps and start grid ref: NT car park – OS Landranger 182 & Explorer 141 –
grid ref: ST488340

Cheddar Gorge

Circular walk, 5 miles (8 km)

At almost 400 feet deep and three miles long, this is England's
largest gorge, and with its weathered crags and pinnacles, one
of our most spectacular natural sights. It plays host to a varied
community of specialised plants and wildlife, many of which you'll
get the chance to spot on this exhilarating circular walk.

Maps and start grid ref: Cheddar Tourist Information Centre – grid ref: ST468543 – OS
Landranger map 182

Sand Point & Middlehope

Coastal walk, 4 miles (6.4 km)

A bracing walk which culminates at Sand Point, a limestone
extension of the Mendip Hills which juts into the Bristol Channel.
There are wonderful views across to Wales, as well as wildlife and
archaeological interest along the way.

Maps and start grid ref: OS Landranger 182gr ST330659, Explorer 153

Selworthy Beacon, Exmoor

Coastal walk, 7 miles (11.2 km)

This truly spectacular walk over moorland takes in breathtaking
views of the Somerset coast and the Mendips, parts of Devon, the
Bristol Channel and the south Wales coast. There is wildlife interest
at all times of the year.

Maps and start grid ref: OS Landranger 181 grSS911477, Explorer OL 9

Wiltshire

Calstone Coombes

Countryside walk, 4 miles (6.4 km)

Welcome to countryside free of traffic noise where you can enjoy
the call of meadow pipits and skylarks, and wander in solitude.
This route leads through the lonely winding coombes of north
Wiltshire's chalk downland – a wildlife-rich area and the perfect
place to escape to at the weekend.

Maps and start grid ref: Calstone – Ranscombe Bottom – maps: OS Landranger 173 –
grid ref: SU045685

Dinton Park

Countryside walk, 2 miles (3.2 km)

Explore a tranquil, historic parkland on this gentle walk secluded
within the Nadder Valley. You'll uncover a grand neo-Classical

house, an ornamental lake and plenty of wildlife. Listen out for woodpeckers in the woodland and admire spectacular views across the Wiltshire countryside towards the cathedral city of Salisbury.

Maps and start grid ref: NT car park – grid ref: SU 004319 – maps: Explorer 130 & Landranger 184

Stourhead - Park Hill Camp walk

Circular route, 3 miles (4.8 km)

Discover the Park Hill Camp Walk – a circular route that leads through magnificent woodland dotted with snowdrops in winter and thronged with bluebells later in the year. See an Iron Age fort and medieval deer park and enjoy Stourhead's renowned gardens.

Maps and start grid ref: Stourhead National Trust car park – grid ref: ST 780340 – OS Landranger 183

Stonehenge Landscape

3½ miles (5.6 km)

This walk explores chalk downland at the heart of the Stonehenge World Heritage Site. From Bronze Age burial mounds to ancient ceremonial pathways, the landscape surrounding Britain's most famous prehistoric monument is full of intriguing archaeology. There's also a fantastic array of wildlife to look out for.

Maps and start and finish grid ref: Stonehenge car park – grid ref: SU120420 – OS Landranger 184 or Explorer 130 maps

WEST MIDLANDS

Herefordshire

Brockhampton

Wildlife walk, 1½ miles (2.4 km)

Brockhampton, near Bromyard in Herefordshire is a special place to visit throughout the year with its orchards, meadows and woods that change with the seasons and attract different wildlife. Listen for the deep croak of ravens, woodpeckers tapping trees, and enjoy the bluebells, primroses, wild daffodils and the eye-catching insects associated with the old trees on the estate.

Maps and start grid ref: OS Landranger 149: SO682546. Maps of circular walks are available at the estate

Berrington Park

2 miles (3.2 km)

Berrington Park was one of 'Capability' Brown's finest landscapes. His vision was to create the perfect setting for the house, which provides visitors with stunning views to Wales and the Black Mountains. Note the walk is only open from March to December.

Maps and start grid ref: Triumphal Arch at Berrington Hall – OS map: 149 – grid ref: SO 509636

Staffordshire

Downs Bank

1½ (2.4 km) or 2 miles (3.2 km)

This little wilderness of woodlands and heath in the heart of the West Midlands is a fantastic place to explore with your dog. Take a little exercise and enjoy the fresh air on this walk alongside the stream, or if you're both feeling energetic, add half a mile more and climb uphill for fantastic panoramic views.

Maps and start grid ref: NT Downs Banks car park – grid ref: SJ900365 – OS Landranger 127

Worcestershire

Clent Hills

1 mile (1.6 km)

The Clent Hills have been enjoyed by day-trippers from nearby Midlands towns and cities for over 200 years. This short walk leads through woodland to the top of a hill where on a clear day the Welsh Black Mountains are visible on the horizon. Visitors in spring will see the hillside and woodland floor coloured lilac by bluebells.

Map and start grid ref: OS Explorer 219, SO 938807.

YORKSHIRE & NORTH EAST

Northumberland

Allen Banks & Staward Gorge

Woodland wildlife walk, 2½ miles (4 km)

Explore these fine ancient woodlands set on the steep valley sides of the river Allen, a tributary of the South Tyne. Look out for a fantastic variety of flora, fauna and fungi on this gentle walk at Allen Banks.

Maps and start grid ref: Allen Banks car park – grid ref: NY799640 – OS maps: Landranger 86/87, Explorer OL 43

Craster to Low Newton by-the-Sea

Coastal walk, 6 miles (9.6 km)

This coastline is famed for its wide-open spaces and dramatic skies. Along the walk you'll pass the majestic Dunstanburgh Castle and witness a rich variety of birds and flowers around Embleton and Newton Links.

Maps and start grid ref: Craster – Map & grid ref: OS Landranger 75, NU 258201

Farne Islands

Wildlife walk, ½ mile (0.8 km)

The rocky shores of the Farne Islands are a haven for seals and sea birds, but there is also a fascinating history to unearth on this gentle half mile circular route.

Maps and start grid ref: OS Landranger 75 – NU 230370

Wallington

Red squirrel walk, 2 miles (3.2 km)

This walk meanders through woodland wth a wildlife observation hide, red squirrel feeders (food is bought with donations left by visitors) and stunning views of the Wansbeck river valley.

Maps and start grid ref: OS Landranger 81, gr NZ 029 842, Explorer OL29

North Yorkshire

Upper Wharfedale

Wildlife walk 6 miles (9.6 km)

A glorious walk in the Yorkshire Dales. Discover an exciting landscape of limestone pavement, glaciated valleys, fast-flowing streams and flower-filled hay meadows.

Maps and start grid ref: OS Landranger 98: SD904790

A view of Cray in the Upper Wharfedale Valley. (North Yorkshire)

West Yorkshire

Hardcastle Crags

Woodland wildlife walk, 3 miles (4.8 km)

The valleys of Hardcastle Crags, west of Halifax, offer stunning riverside views while the oak, beech and pine woods are full of tumbling streams. Whether you decide to climb the rocky paths to the hilltops or enjoy a picnic by old weirs, there's plenty of wildlife to see.

Maps and start grid ref: Midgehole car park – grid ref: SD 988291 – map: OS Explorer OL21

WALES

Snowdonia and Llyn Peninsula

Craflwyn and the Nant Gwynant

Hillside walk, 3¾ miles (5 km)

One of Wales' most spectacular valleys, Nant Gwynant is encircled by high mountains, with Snowdon rising up to the north. This exhilarating walk explores an historic landscape, rich in Dark Age legend, with the remains of 19th-century copper mining lining much of the route. Enjoy dramatic waterfalls, great views and the chance to spot a variety of wildlife as you climb up through the National Trust's Hafod Y Llan farm, cross the hillside and descend to Craflwyn, a Victorian hall and estate.

Maps and start grid ref: Bethania – OS Explorer 17 map – grid ref: SH 599489

Aberdaron to Mynydd Mawr

Coastal walk, 6 miles (9.6 km)

This walk takes in coast that is very special for its birds, plants and diverse landforms and has a fascinating history linked with Ynys Enlli (Bardsey), the legendary 'Isle of 20,000 Saints'.

Maps and start grid ref: OS Landranger 123 G.R. SH174264, Explorer 253

Carreg Y Llam

Coastal walk, 3 miles (4.8 km)

From the north a stunning vista appears before you as the slopes of the mountains of Moel Gwynus and Moel Ty Gwyn descend to a distinctive plateau known as a drift terrace. Spring is superb with good displays of flora like lady's smock, primrose and early purple orchid. Buzzards regularly hunt over the property but smaller birds like yellowhammer and linnets can be seen. Not all sections are on National Trust land.

Maps and start grid ref: OS Landranger 123 gr SH 329422, Explorer 253

Porth Dinllaen

Coastal walk, 2 miles (3.2 km)

The hamlet of Porth Dinllaen is situated on a beautiful stretch of coastline with a sandy beach fringed by cliffs and ragged coastline. The National Trust acquired this special area in 1994 using Neptune funds for its historic and seafaring history and for its geological and marine interest. There are 16 houses, the Ty Coch Inn, and the RNLI station all under the care of the National Trust.

Maps and start grid ref: OS Landranger 123 gr SH 281406, Explorer 253

Low tide at Porth Oer. (Gwynedd)

Porthor to Mynydd Anelog

Coastal walk, 5½ miles (8.8 km)

Porthor and the two hills of Mynydd Carreg and Mynydd Anelog are the main focal points of National Trust land in this area consisting of over 170 ha of shoreline, headland and farmland. This beautiful walk gives an insight into Llyn's traditional farming, wildlife, diverse habitats and fascinating geology. Porthor is also known as the 'Whistling Sands' as the rounded grains of sand 'squeak' or whistle underfoot. Note that not all sections are on National Trust land.

Maps and start grid ref: OS Landranger 123 gr SH166296, Explorer 253

Camarthenshire

Dinefwr

Wildlife walk, 3 miles (4.8 km)

Dinefwr's historic parkland is famed for its abundance of wildlife and stunning valley views. Some of the 'veteran' trees are thought to be over 700 years old and support such a high diversity of lichens and invertebrates that the park has been declared a Site of Special Scientific Interest. In July 2007 it also became a National Nature Reserve – the only parkland NNR in Wales. This walk takes in some of the estate's great wildlife-spotting places, as well as a fascinating medieval castle and 17th-century mansion.

Starting point: Dinefwr Park is 1m (1.6km) from the centre of Llandeilo in south Wales, just off the A40 and half a mile from Llandeilo railway station.

Gower Peninsula

Rhossili Bay

Coastal walk, 5 miles (8 km)

Take in the tremendous coastal views from Rhossili Down before descending to Rhossili Bay, considered one of the finest sandy beaches in the UK. At the southern end of the bay, when the tide is low, a finger of limestone rock leads to Worms Head where seabirds and seals can be seen.

Maps and start grid ref: Rhossili National Trust visitor centre – grid ref: SS415879 – OS Landranger map 159

Bishopston Valley

Coastal walk, 3½ miles (5.6 km)

A beautiful mile walk along the Gower south coast, which highlights natural habitats and their wildlife as well as the area's industrial past of mineral mining and quarrying.

Maps and start grid ref: OS Landranger 159 gr SS554874, Explorer 164

Penmaen Burrows

Coastal walk, 2½ miles (4 km)

A short walk in the Three Cliff bay area along a beautiful stretch of the Gower coast full of history. Part of the walk can be taken along the beach if the tide is more than half out.

Maps and start grid ref: OS Landranger 159 gr SS526884, Explorer 164

Rhossili Bay on the Gower Peninsula in south Wales, with Rhossili Down on the right. (Swansea)

Pennard Cliffs

Coastal walk, 3½ miles (5.6 km)

This walk in the Three Cliff bay area travels along a beautiful stretch of the Gower coast with views right across the Bristol Channel to Devon and Somerset. In spring and early summer, wild flowers are in abundance.

Maps and start grid ref: OS Landranger 159 gr SS554874, Explorer 164

Whiteford Burrows

Gower Peninsula walk, 4 miles (6.4 km)

A lovely walk on a large expanse of dunes in the more remote part of North Gower overlooking the estuary of the River Loughor.

Maps and start grid ref: OS Landranger 159 gr SS440933 Explorer 164

41

Pembrokeshire

Stackpole Estate

Wildlife walk, 6 miles (9.6 km)

Either 3½ miles one-way or a 6-mile circular walk set in the stunning scenery of Pembrokeshire National Park. See and smell colonies of breeding seabirds at Stackpole Head. If you're lucky you might also spot an otter at the tranquil lily ponds.

Maps and start grid ref: OS Landranger 158: SR992958 (Stackpole Quay); SR977938 (Broadhaven South); SR968947 (Bosherton Lily Ponds)

Ynys Barri, Porthgain to Abereiddi

Coastal walk, 4 miles (6.4 km)

Enjoy some of Pembrokeshire's finest coastal scenery while exploring its industrial past. The tiny fishing port of Porthgain used to export road stone all over the UK, while Abereiddi's famous Blue Lagoon was once an old slate quarry. Ynys Barri (or Barry Island) is also home to a fantastic array of wildlife.

Maps and start grid ref: Porthgain – OS Landranger 157 & Explorer OL 35 map – grid ref: SM816325

St David's Head

Coastal walk, 3¾ miles (13.2 km)

Explore Pembrokeshire's most spectacular coastal headland several miles away from Wales' smallest city, St David's. Look out at island-dotted seascapes against the steep backdrop of Carn Llidi, prehistoric monuments and a fantastic array of coastal wildlife on this rugged circular walk.

Maps and start grid ref: Whitesands Beach car park – OS Landranger 157 map – grid ref: SM734272

NORTHERN IRELAND

County Down

Mount Stewart

Red squirrel walk, 1.4 miles (2.2km)

Some of Ireland's last remaining red squirrels find sanctuary in the lovely formal and informal gardens at Mount Stewart. This walk also takes in sweeping views over Strangford Lough towards the Mourne mountains.

Maps and start grid ref: OS 1:50,000 sheet 15, gr J 553 701

Castle Ward and Strangford Lough

Loughside walk, 2½ miles (4 km)

Overlooking the south shores of Strangford Lough, Castle Ward is one of Northern Ireland's finest *demesnes* or country estates. At its heart lies an unusual Georgian mansion, but there is a lot more to discover here. This walk explores the waterside, a ruined castle, woodland, an ornamental lake and follies. Visit in winter for a chance to see a fantastic range of migrating birds and the resident seals.

Maps and start grid ref: Old Castle Ward farmyard – grid ref: J753498 – OS NI Discoverer map 21

County Fermanagh

Crom

Wildlife walk, 3½ miles (5.6 km)

Discover a tranquil landscape of islands, woodland and historic ruins, on the shores of Upper Lough Erne in County Fermanagh. Crom is one of the UK's most important nature reserves, with the largest area of oak woodland in Northern Ireland. Wildlife includes wading birds, bats, pine martens and a thriving otter population.

Maps and start grid ref:OS Discoverer 27: H332 2442. Simple NT maps available

Top Ten Wildlife Walks

The National Trust's conservation experts have chosen ten of their favourite places to go for a walk and get close to nature. From hillsides to historic parks, they all offer a chance to discover the UK's finest wildlife and habitats. Every season offers the walker something new: try a walk in summer and return in winter for a totally different wildlife experience.

Arnside Knott, Cumbria Coast
see page 24
- Listen for the loud 'pichoo' call of the marsh tit in the woodland.
- Look out for rare butterflies.

Ashridge Estate, Hertfordshire
see page 27
- Look out for gliding red kites above and the striking six-spot burnet moth.
- Ashridge is famed for its bluebells in spring and vibrant autumnal colour later in the year.

Brockhampton Estate, Herefordshire *see page 35*
- Look for invertebrates and fungi living in dead wood.
- Listen for woodpeckers drumming on trees and the deep croak of ravens.

Brownsea Island, Dorset
see page 29
- Has a Red squirrel colony.
- Many species of wader bird and duck are found here.
- Look for the Dragonfly and damselfly and the scarce bird's nest orchid.

Calke Park and Abbey, Derbyshire *see page 20*
- Keep your eyes open for signs of badgers in the woods and dragonflies on the ponds.

Crom, Northern Ireland
see page 43
- Look out for bats and the elusive pine marten.

Cubert, Cornwall *see page 14*
- Here you will find sand dune invertebrates like the striped-wing grasshopper, to everyone's favourite grey seals.
- Don't miss the summer display of bright poppies and marigolds.

Harting Down, South Downs
see page 26
- Catch a whiff of the blooming juniper bushes.
- Listen out for singing nightingales and skylarks.

Stackpole Estate, Pembrokeshire *see page 42*
- See and smell colonies of breeding seabirds at Stackpole Head.
- If you're very very lucky you might spot an otter around the tranquil lilyponds.

Upper Wharfedale, North Yorkshire *see page 36*
- Lots of unusual plants live on the 'clints' and in the 'grikes'....
- The clean waters of the River Wharfe are great for fish, insects and birdlife.

Red Squirrel at Brownsea Island

Braich-y-Pwll near Aberdaron, looking across towards
Mynydd Anelog in the distance. (Gwynedd)

Location

Date

Location

Date

Location

Date

Location

Date

Location

Date

Location

Date

Location ....

....

Date ....

....

....

....

....

....

....

....

....

....

....

....

....

....

....

....

....

A puffin on the Farne Islands. (Northumberland)

Location

Date

Location

Date

Location

Date

Location

Date

Location

Date

Location

Date

Location

Date

White ducks at Lyveden New Bield, Peterborough. (Northamptonshire)

Location

Date

Location

Date

Location

Date

Location

Date

Location

Date

Location

Date

Location ....

....

Date ....

....

....

....

....

....

....

....

....

....

....

....

....

....

....

....

....

Location

Date

Location

Date

Rowing boat on Loweswater in the Buttermere Valley. (Cumbria)

Location

Date

Location

Date

Location

Date

Location

Date

Location

Date

Location

Date

Location

Date

The Nant Gwynant Valley from Hafod Y Llan farm, Snowdonia. (Gwynedd)

80

Location

Date

Location

Date

Location ....

....

Date ....

....

....

....

....

....

....

....

....

....

....

....

....

....

....

....

....

Location

Date

Location

Date

Location

Date

Location ....

....

Date ....

....

....

....

....

....

....

....

....

....

....

....

....

....

....

....

....

....

....

Location

....

....

Date

....

....

....

....

....

....

....

....

....

....

....

....

....

....

....

....

....

Overleaf: The bridge over the millstream at sunset at Flatford Mill. (Suffolk)

Location

Date

Location

Date

Location

Date

Location

Date

Location

Date

Location

Date

Location

Date

Location

Date

Location ....

....

Date ....

....

....

....

....

....

....

....

Snowdon summits on the edge of Galli Iago Farm. (Gwynedd)

Location

Date

Location

Date

Location

Date

Location

Date

Location

Date

Location

Date

Location

Date

Bluebells (*Hyacinthoides non-scripta*) at Leith Hill Place, Dorking. (Surrey)

Location

Date

Location

Date

Location ....

....

Date ....

....

....

....

....

....

....

....

....

....

....

....

....

....

....

....

....

....

....

....

Location

Date

Location

Date

Location

Date

Location ....

....

Date ....

....

....

....

....

....

....

....

....

....

....

....

....

....

....

....

....

....

Location

Date

Location ....

....

Date ....

....

....

....

....

....

....

....

....

....

....

....

....

....

....

....

....

....

....

Fallow deer stag at Crom Estate. (Co. Fermanagh)

Location

Date

Location

Date

Location

Date

Location

Date

Location ....

....

Date ....

....

....

....

....

....

....

....

....

....

....

....

....

....

....

....

....

Location

Date

Location ....

....

Date ....

....

....

....

....

....

....

....

....

....

....

....

....

....

....

....

....

....

View of Dunstanburgh Castle. (Northumberland)

Location

Date

Location

Date

Location

Date

Location

Date

Location

Date

Location ....

....

Date ....

....

....

....

....

....

....

....

....

....

....

....

....

....

....

....

....

Overleaf: Wooden bridge over Burbage Brook on Longshaw estate.
(Derbyshire & Peak District)

Location

Date

Location

Date

Location

Date

Location

Date

Location

Date

Location

Date

Location ....

....

Date ....

Waterfall at Hardcastle Crags. (West Yorkshire)

Location

Date

Location

Date

Location

Date

Location

Date

Location

Date

Location

Date

Location

....

....

Date

....

A Konik pony (Tarpan wild horse) at Wicken Fen. (Cambridgeshire)

PICTURE CREDITS